Sing a Song
OF SEASONS

Five easy-to-perform plays for pre-school and early years learning

BRIAN OGDEN

Brian Ogden was for many years a teacher and RE advisor for the dioceses of Peterborough and Chelmsford. He is author of many popular books in the Barnabas range, including News and Tell!, Year-Round Assemblies, Starting Together *and* Nursery Rhyme Nativities. *Brian is a regular speaker in schools, typically sharing his stories and his work with more than 7,000 children in the course of a year.*

Text copyright © Brian Ogden 2005
Illustrations copyright © Marie Allen 2005
The author asserts the moral right
to be identified as the author of this work

Published by
The Bible Reading Fellowship
First Floor, Elsfield Hall
15–17 Elsfield Way, Oxford OX2 8FG
Website: www.brf.org.uk

ISBN 1 84101 364 1
First published 2005
10 9 8 7 6 5 4 3 2 1 0

Acknowledgments
Unless otherwise stated, scripture quotations are taken from the Contemporary English Version of the Bible published by HarperCollins Publishers, copyright © 1991, 1992, 1995 American Bible Society.

Performance and copyright
The right to perform *Sing a Song of Seasons* drama material is included in the purchase price, so long as the performance is in an amateur context, for instance in church services, schools or holiday club venues. Where any charge is made to audiences, written permission must be obtained from the author, who can be contacted through the publishers. A fee or royalties may be payable for the right to perform the script in that context.

A catalogue record for this book is available from the British Library

Printed in Singapore by Craft Print International Ltd

CONTENTS

FOREWORD

During the last three years, I have worked alongside Brian Ogden at days for schools at Norwich and Ely Cathedrals. It has been a very enlightening experience to watch the children—especially those with special needs—responding to his stories, jokes, and gifts as a Christian author. This year we decided to experiment by putting on *Growing Up* from this book as a play-in-a-day at Ely, with 100 children. The Key Stage 1 children practised the songs and drama, and made the puppets and scenery. The presentation was very successful and was enjoyed by all the children and adults.

The plays in *Sing a Song of Seasons* are all written in a way that allows teachers to adapt them to suit the needs of their children and school. Brian realizes children's affinity with animals, and is able to convey this through ingenious rhymes and phrases. The ideas for props, costumes and puppets are effective and easy to use, but allow scope for creativity. The humour in the songs and the simplicity of the narration blend well to capture the attention of the children and audience.

As I read through the draft copies of these plays, I realized that if the children had the experience of performing in all of them in their early years in school, they would gain a sound idea of God's message to the world—the message of love, forgiveness and hope.

I hope you enjoy using this book with your children, and I am sure you will catch the humour and sincere enthusiasm that Brian wishes to share.

Kate Clodd (KS1 teacher, school governor and music specialist)

INTRODUCTION

This book contains five separate simple plays for use with Foundation/Reception and Key Stage One children. In each play the stories are told through story and song. It is assumed that children will mime the story alongside the narration and songs.

NARRATORS

The narration in each play is fundamental. It is essential that those chosen to narrate are very able readers with voices that are sufficiently powerful for the occasion. Working with young children, the timing of the narration is also crucial. Unless there are older children who can fulfil these requirements, it is better to use adult narrators. It may be appropriate to change the narrators during any particular presentation.

THE SONGS

The songs are all written to popular tunes, mostly nursery rhymes, which will be familiar to the children. It is very helpful for the overall success of the presentation if the words are made available to

all attending the presentation. This may be done as printed wordsheets or on overhead projector (OHP) acetates. For ease of photocopying, a complete set of the songs may be found in Appendix One. The participation of the audience is a vital aspect of each play. It not only adds to the overall enjoyment but also encourages and supports the children.

A simple score of the music of the tunes used for the songs can be found in Appendix Two. Many of the songs are interchangeable between plays. If one song appeals more than another, then an exchange can be made.

THE CHILDREN

These plays are designed to involve either a small or large number of children. If there are few children, there will be no difficulty in giving all the children acting parts. If numbers are higher, then the remainder can very usefully form a choir. It may be that the older children in the school can fulfil this role.

STAGING

The word 'stage' has been used throughout to indicate the acting area. Circumstances vary enormously but provision should be made for movement on and off the acting area, ideally by way of access from either side. Any movement by characters in the plays is indicated in the stage directions by italics. Each play is written with school halls, churches or any large room in mind.

COSTUMES AND PROPS

Decisions over costumes and props must be left to individual users. The most important factor must always be the safety of the children, especially regarding the length of any garments worn. Much can be done by the use of simple masks or cardboard cut-outs.

Lengths of frieze rolls can be used to make simple and cost-effective backgrounds. Suggestions for backgrounds are given in the introductions to the individual plays. Props are also suggested for each play. To help with your preparation, templates can be found in Appendix Three for some of the props and costume masks. Items included are listed in the Contents on page 3.

CHILDREN'S WORK

There are several opportunities to involve the children in the preparation of each play. Some of the friezes will require painting. Items such as birds, clouds and masks will need to be made. In some of the plays, children may wish to write their own verses to some of the songs.

PRESENTATION

These plays are designed to be fun to perform, and this should be achieved without a huge amount of preparation. Strong adult participation in the singing will enable the children to concentrate on the acting and help to create an act of worship. Traditional hymns or songs may be used at the beginning or end of a performance and you may wish to end the presentation with a prayer.

THE PLAYS

You will find all the stories for the plays in the Bible. The wording of the scripts uses the Contemporary English Version.

A celebration of creation

The narration in this play is based on the creation narrative in Genesis 1:3—2:4. The play is intended to be a simple celebration of creation with plenty of fun songs and movements.

Palm trees to Easter gardens

This play tells the story of the events from Palm Sunday to Easter Day in a simple way. Although much of the action is omitted, it is intended that through the drama and the songs the children should gain an understanding of the events of Holy Week and Easter. Whereas the story of these events is told in all four Gospels, the words in this play are mostly based on the accounts in the Gospels of Mark and John. The passages used are Mark 11:1–8; Mark 14:12–16 and 32–50; John 13:3–12; John 18:28—19:42 and John 20:11–18.

Sad dad to glad dad!

This play is based on the parable of the prodigal son in Luke 15:11–32. The aim is to introduce the concept of forgiveness while providing drama and songs for younger children. The play may be used at any time of the year, but would be an appropriate presentation towards the end of the summer term.

A place in the sun

This play is based on the parable of the two builders in Matthew 7:24–27. It would be an appropriate presentation for the end of the summer term or at any other time in the year.

Growing up

This play is based on the parable of the farmer in Mark 4:3–8. It is especially appropriate at harvest time, but could just as well be used at other times of the year, especially in the spring term.

A CELEBRATION OF CREATION

This story is taken from Genesis 1:3—2:4.

CAST AND PROPS

in order of appearance

Adult to introduce the play
Narrators 1 and 2
Children dressed in white
Children dressed in black
Black frieze paper for background
White frieze paper for background
Water frieze (A) (blue, showing waves and 'white horses')
Sky frieze (B) (light blue)
Land frieze (C) (green)
Words:
- DAY (black text on white paper)
- NIGHT (white text on black paper)
- SKY (black text on a cloud shape)
- LAND
- SEA
- EVENING
- MORNING

Clouds on canes (various shapes/colours)
Sun, moon and stars on canes
Birds on canes
Torches
Masks or costumes for plants (or model plants/trees to carry on stage)
Masks or costumes for sea creatures
Masks or costumes for animals

Adult introduction

We are here to celebrate the creation of the world. You will find the story that leads us through the drama in the very first book of the Bible—in the very first chapter of Genesis. The story does not represent a period of 24 hours so much as a celebration of what God has created over a period of time.

In the beginning God created the heavens and the earth. The earth was under a roaring ocean covered with darkness, but the Spirit of God was moving over the water.

SCENE ONE (DAY ONE)

The whole scene takes place in front of a totally black background. This can best be achieved by a length of black frieze paper wound on to a roller. Half the children should be dressed in white and half in black.

Narrator 1: And God said, 'I command the light to shine!' And light started shining.

Children enter slowly one at a time. Those in white shine torches haphazardly on to the black background.

Narrator 2: God looked at the light and saw that it was good.

☆ SONG ONE ☆

It was good

(Tune: The farmer's in his den)

The light is shining bright,
The light is shining bright,
God saw that it was good,
The light is shining bright.

Narrator 1: God separated the light from darkness.

Slowly the two groups of children separate. Those in white unroll a white frieze roll, which covers half of the black background. The children move in front of their own colour.

Narrator 2: He named the light 'Day'...

The word DAY in black letters is fixed to the white background.

Narrator 1: ... and he named the darkness 'Night'.

The word NIGHT in white letters is fixed to the black background.

☆ SONG TWO ☆

Night and day

(Tune: Jack and Jill)

The first verse is sung by children dressed in black, the second verse by children dressed in white. All join in the last verse.

All was black, and all was dark,
When God began creation,
Nothing could be seen at all,
There was no variation.

Let light shine, commanded God,
And soon the light was shining.
Light is day, the dark is night *(line sung in two halves by the two groups)*,
It's part of my designing.

Thanks to God we have them still,
It's part of his plan for us;
So alleluia, praise the Lord,
Let all join in this chorus.

Narrator 2: Evening came... and then morning—that was the first day.

Two children enter, the first carrying the word EVENING and (after a pause) the second carrying the word MORNING.

SCENE TWO (DAY TWO)

As the 'EVENING' and 'MORNING' children leave, other children slowly unroll the 'water' frieze (A).

Narrator 1: God said, 'I command a dome to separate the water above it from the water below it.'

During Song Three the water frieze is lowered to an angle of about 45 degrees to enable the sky frieze (B) to be lifted behind it. In between the two friezes, children move slowly across the stage with clouds on canes. At the end of the song, the word SKY is held high against the blue sky frieze.

★ SONG THREE ★

Sky-sea song

(Tune: London Bridge is falling down)

Lots of water everywhere,
Everywhere, everywhere,
Lots of water everywhere,
Make a dome now.

Place the sky high in the heavens,
In the heavens, in the heavens,
Place the sky high in the heavens,
Above the water.

Let clouds float across the sky,
Across the sky, across the sky,
Let clouds float across the sky,
High in the heavens.

Narrator 2: And that's what happened. God made the dome and named it 'Sky'.

★ SONG ONE (REPRISE) ★

It was good

(Tune: The farmer's in his den)

The sky is in the heavens,
The sky is in the heavens,
God saw that it was good,
The sky is in the heavens.

Narrator 1: Evening came… and then morning—that was the second day.

Two children enter, the first carrying the word EVENING and (after a pause) the second carrying the word MORNING.

SCENE THREE (DAY THREE)

The 'EVENING' and 'MORNING' children leave.

Narrator 2: God said, 'I command the water under the sky to come together in one place, so there will be dry ground.'

The water frieze (A) is rolled up so that only a small length shows. The land frieze (C) is unrolled, filling up the space left by the water frieze.

Narrator 1: And that's what happened. God named the dry ground 'Land', and he named the water 'Sea'.

The two words LAND and SEA are fixed to the friezes.

Narrator 2: God looked at what he had done and saw that it was good.

★ SONG ONE (REPRISE) ★

It was good

(Tune: The farmer's in his den)

God made the land and sea,
God made the land and sea,
God saw that they were good,
God made the land and sea.

Narrator 1: God said, 'I command the earth to produce all kinds of plants, including fruit trees and grain.'

Children stand up behind the land frieze (C) wearing masks or carrying plants, fruit trees, grain and so on, as Song Four is sung.

★ SONG FOUR ★

The plant song

(Tune: Old MacDonald had a farm)

Father God he made the land,
Praise, oh praise his name!
And on this land he grew some plants,
Praise, oh praise his name!
With a rose bush here,
A busy lizzie there,
Here a plant, there a plant,
Everywhere another plant.
Father God he made the land,
Praise, oh praise his name!

Father God he made the land,
Praise, oh praise his name!
And on this land he grew some trees,
Praise, oh praise his name!
With an apple tree here,

A cherry tree there,
Here some fruit, there some fruit,
Everywhere some other fruit.
Father God he made the land,
Praise, oh praise his name!

Father God he made the land,
Praise, oh praise his name!
And on this land he grew some grain,
Praise, oh praise his name!
With a wheat field here,
And a maize field there,
Here some corn, there some corn,
Everywhere golden corn.
Father God he made the land,
Praise, oh praise his name!

Narrator 2: And that's what happened. The earth produced all kinds of vegetation.
Narrator 1: God looked at what he had done, and it was good.
Narrator 2: Evening came… and then morning—that was the third day.

Land frieze (C) is rolled up. Two children enter, the first carrying the word EVENING and (after a pause) the second carrying the word MORNING.

SCENE FOUR (DAY FOUR)

The 'EVENING' and 'MORNING' children leave.

Narrator 1: God said, 'I command lights to appear in the sky and to separate day from night…
Narrator 2: … and to show the time for seasons, special days and years. I command them to shine on the earth.'
Narrator 1: And that's what happened. God made two powerful lights, the brighter one to rule the day…

⭐ SONG FIVE ⭐

The sun and the moon song

(Tune: Michael Finnegan)

Each verse to be sung three times, each time getting quicker.

And God commanded, 'Do what I say again,
A light, very bright, to shine in the day again.'
He looked at the light and said, 'OK' again,
In God's perfect way again, shine again.

Sky frieze (B) is unrolled. Child enters with brightly painted sun on a cane, walks slowly across the stage and stops at the side.

Narrator 2: … and the other to rule the night.

I need a light that's not so bright again,
A light, not so bright, to shine in the night again,
He looked at the light and said, 'That's right' again,
Up there in the height again, shine again.

Sun is lowered. Second child enters past the sun with moon on a cane and walks slowly across to the other side.

Narrator 1: He also made the stars.

Up in the sky God fixed tiny stars again,
Saturn, Jupiter, Venus and Mars again,
Then he shouted 'hip hip hoorahs' again.
With extra loud 'oompahs' again, shine again.

Moon returns to centre stage. Enter lots of children with stars on canes of different heights. They move around on either side of the moon.

Narrator 2: Then God put these lights in the sky to shine on the earth, to rule day and night, and to separate light from darkness.
Narrator 1: God looked at what he had done, and it was good.

⭐ SONG ONE (REPRISE) ⭐

It was good

(Tune: The farmer's in his den)

God made the sun and moon,
God made the sun and moon,
God saw that they were good,
God made the sun and moon.

Narrator 2: Evening came… and then morning—that was the fourth day.

Two children enter, the first carrying the word EVENING and (after a pause) the second carrying the word MORNING.

SCENE FIVE (DAY FIVE)

The 'EVENING' and 'MORNING' children leave.

Narrator 1: God said, 'I command the sea to be full of living creatures…
Narrator 2: and I command birds to fly above the earth.'

The water and land friezes (A) and (C) are unrolled, each filling half of the stage area.

Narrator 1: So God made the sea monsters and all the living creatures that swim in the sea.

Narrator 2: He also made every kind of bird.

Children dressed as sea creatures, or with masks or cut-out pictures, move around behind the water frieze. Children either wearing masks or with cut-out birds on canes move in front of the sky frieze.

★ SONG SIX ★

The sea creatures and birds

(Tune: Green grow the rushes-o)

'Sea' and 'Sky' children sing their own verses or lines.

'Sea' children
We'll sing you one-o,
Deep are the oceans-o.
What is your one-o?
One's a shark with big white teeth and ever more shall be so.

'Sky' children
We'll sing you two-o,
High are the heavens-o.
What are your two-o?
Two's a blackbird in a tree, singing all the day-o.

'Sea' children
One's a shark with big white teeth and ever more shall be so.

'Sea' children
We'll sing you three-o,
Deep are the oceans-o.
What are your three-o?
Three, three, the turtle.

'Sky' children
Two's a blackbird in a tree, singing all the day-o.

'Sea' children
One's a shark with big white teeth and ever more shall be so:

'Sky' children
We'll sing you four-o,
High are the heavens-o.
What are your four-o?
Four for the eagle flying high.

'Sea' children
Three, three, the turtle.

'Sky' children
Two's a blackbird in a tree, singing all the day-o.

'Sea' children
One's a shark with big white teeth and ever more shall be so.

'Sea' children
We'll sing you five-o,
Deep are the oceans-o.
What are your five-o?
Five for the dolphin playing tricks,

'Sky' children
And four for the eagle flying high.

'Sea' children
Three, three, the turtle.

'Sky' children
Two's a blackbird in a tree, singing all the day-o.

'Sky' children
One's a shark with big white teeth and ever more shall be so.

'Sky' children
We'll sing you six-o,
High are the heavens-o.
What are your six-o?
Six for the six swooping swallows,

'Sea' children
Five for the dolphin playing tricks,

'Sky' children
And four for the eagle flying high.

'Sea' children
Three, three, the turtle.

'Sky' children
Two's a blackbird in a tree, singing all the day-o.

'Sea' children
One's a shark with big white teeth and ever more shall be so.

'Sea' children
We'll sing you seven-o,
Deep are the oceans-o,
What are your seven-o?
Seven for the seven whales swimming deep,

'Sky' children
And six for the six swooping swallows,

'Sea' children
Five for the dolphin playing tricks,

'Sky' children
And four for the eagle flying high.

'Sea' children
Three, three, the turtle.

'Sky' children
Two's a blackbird in a tree, singing all the day-o.

'Sea' children
One's a shark with big white teeth and ever more shall be so.

'Sky' children
We'll sing you eight-o,
High are the heavens-o,
What are your eight-o?
Eight for the robin redbreast,

'Sea' children
Seven for the seven whales swimming deep,

'Sky' children
And six for the six swooping swallows,

'Sea' children
Five for the dolphin playing tricks,

'Sky' children
And four for the eagle flying high.

'Sea' children
Three, three, the turtle.

'Sky' children
Two's a blackbird in a tree, singing all the day-o.

'Sea' children
One's a shark with big white teeth and ever more shall be so.

'Sea' children
We'll sing you nine-o,
Deep are the oceans-o.
What are your nine-o?
Nine for the nine crawling crabs,

'Sky' children
Eight for the robin redbreast,

'Sea' children
Seven for the seven whales swimming deep,

'Sky' children
And six for the six swooping swallows,

'Sea' children
Five for the dolphin playing tricks,

'Sky' children
And four for the eagle flying high.

'Sea' children
Three, three, the turtle.

'Sky' children
Two's a blackbird in a tree, singing all the day-o.

'Sea' children
One's a shark with big white teeth and ever more shall be so.

'Sky' children
We'll sing you ten-o,
High are the heavens-o.
What are your ten-o?
Ten for the ten loud cuckoos,

'Sea' children
Nine for the nine crawling crabs,

'Sky' children
Eight for the robin redbreast,

'Sea' children
Seven for the seven whales swimming deep,

'Sky' children
And six for the six swooping swallows,

'Sea' children
Five for the dolphin playing tricks,

'Sky' children
And four for the eagle flying high.

'Sea' children
Three, three, the turtle.

'Sky' children
Two's a blackbird in a tree, singing all the day-o.

'Sea' children
One's a shark with big white teeth and ever more shall be so.

Narrator 1: God looked at what he had done, and it was good. Then he gave the living creatures his blessing.

Narrator 2: He told the sea creatures to live everywhere in the sea and the birds to live everywhere on earth.

All sing the fifth verse from 'It was good' together:

☆ **SONG ONE (REPRISE)** ☆
....

It was good

(Tune: The farmer's in his den)

God made the fish and birds,
God made the fish and birds,
God saw that they were good,
God made the fish and birds.

Narrator 1: Evening came… and then morning—that was the fifth day.

Water frieze (A) is taken off stage. Land frieze (C) is extended to fill stage. Two children enter, the first carrying the word EVENING and (after a pause) the second carrying the word MORNING.

SCENE SIX (DAY SIX)

The 'EVENING' and 'MORNING' children leave.

Narrator 2: God said, 'I command the earth to give life to all kinds of tame animals, wild animals and reptiles.'

Narrator 1: And that's what happened.

Animals everywhere

(Tune: He's got the whole world in his hands)

Children enter in pairs behind the land frieze (C), dressed as the animals in the song or wearing an appropriate mask.

He made the creepy crawly spider with his hands,
He made the creepy crawly spider with his hands,
He made the creepy crawly spider with his hands,
He made the whole world with his hands.

He made the snugly cuddly rabbit with his hands,
He made the snugly cuddly rabbit with his hands,
He made the snugly cuddly rabbit with his hands,
He made the whole world with his hands.

He made the humpy dumpy camel with his hands,
He made the humpy dumpy camel with his hands,
He made the humpy dumpy camel with his hands,
He made the whole world with his hands.

He made the happy snappy crocodile with his hands,
He made the happy snappy crocodile with his hands,
He made the happy snappy crocodile with his hands,
He made the whole world with his hands.

He made the jumpy bumpy puppy with his hands,
He made the jumpy bumpy puppy with his hands,
He made the jumpy bumpy puppy with his hands,
He made the whole world with his hands.

He made the perky quirky turkey with his hands,
He made the perky quirky turkey with his hands,
He made the perky quirky turkey with his hands,
He made the whole world with his hands.

He made the podgy splodgy piggy with his hands,
He made the podgy splodgy piggy with his hands,
He made the podgy splodgy piggy with his hands,
He made the whole world with his hands.

He made the swinging clinging monkey with his hands,
He made the swinging clinging monkey with his hands,
He made the swinging clinging monkey with his hands,
He made the whole world with his hands.

Children might be encouraged to make up their own verses.

Narrator 2: God made every one of them.
Narrator 1: Then he looked at what he had done, and it was good.

It was good

(Tune: The farmer's in his den)

Sung by all the animals.

God made the animals,
God made the animals,
God saw that they were good,
God made the animals.

Narrator 2: God said, 'Now we will make
humans, and they will be like us…
Narrator 1: We will let them rule the fish, the
birds, and all other living creatures.'
Narrator 2: So God created humans to be like
himself. He made men…

Enter a boy.

Narrator 1: … and women.

Enter a girl.

Narrator 2: God gave them his blessing and
said…
Narrator 1: 'Have a lot of children!'

As many children as possible come on to the stage!

Narrator 2: 'Fill the earth with people and bring
it under your control.'
Narrator 1: God looked at what he had done.
Narrator 2: All of it was very good.

It was good

(Tune: The farmer's in his den)

God made the people too,
God made the people too,
God saw that we were good,
God made the people too.

Narrator 1: Evening came… and then
morning—that was the sixth day.

*The stage is emptied. Two children enter, the first
carrying the word EVENING and (after a pause)
the second carrying the word MORNING.*

Narrator 2: So the heavens and the earth and
everything else were created.
Narrator 1: By the seventh day God had
finished his work, and so he rested.
Narrator 2: God blessed the seventh day and
made it special because on that day
he rested from his work.
Narrator 1: That's how God created the heavens
and the earth.

The seven days of creation

(Tune: The Twelve Days of Christmas)

*All the children join in singing this last song.
Symbols of each day could be held up during the
song.*

On the first day of creation the good Lord gave
away
Light and darkness, night and day.

On the second day of creation the good Lord
gave away
Sky and water,
Light and darkness, night and day.

On the third day of creation the good Lord gave
away
Land, sea and plants,
Sky and water,
Light and darkness, night and day.

On the fourth day of creation the good Lord
gave away
Sun, moon and stars,
Land, sea and plants,
Sky and water,
Light and darkness, night and day.

On the fifth day of creation the good Lord gave
away
Birds and sea creatures,
Sun, moon and stars,
Land, sea and plants,
Sky and water,
Light and darkness, night and day.

On the sixth day of creation the good Lord
gave away
Animals and humans,
Birds and sea creatures,
Sun, moon and stars,
Land, sea and plants,
Sky and water,
Light and darkness, night and day.

On the seventh day of creation the good Lord
gave away,
One day of rest,
Animals and humans,
Birds and sea creatures,
Sun, moon and stars,
Land, sea and plants,
Sky and water,
Light and darkness, night and day.

PALM TREES TO EASTER GARDEN

This story is taken from Mark 11:1–8; Mark 14:12–16 and 32–50; John 13:3–12; John 18:28—19:42 and John 20:11–18.

CAST AND PROPS

in order of appearance

Adult to introduce the play
Narrators 1 and 2
Jesus
Children to form crowd
Peter
John
Other disciples (up to ten)
Water carrier
Two soldiers

Mary Magdalene
Palm branches
Jar of water for water carrier
Table
Bread
Wine (blackcurrant juice)
Towel
Bowl

Adult introduction

In this drama we journey from the joy of Palm Sunday, through the sadness of Good Friday to the wonder of Easter Day.

Only the narrators can be seen at the start of the drama.

Narrator 1: The time had come for Jesus to make his last visit to Jerusalem.

Narrator 2: He sent two of his friends ahead of him.

Narrator 1: 'Go into the next village,' said Jesus. 'There you will find a donkey that has not been ridden. Bring the donkey to me.'

Narrator 2: The two friends of Jesus looked worried about taking a donkey.

Narrator 1: 'If anyone asks what you are doing, tell them that the Lord needs it,' said Jesus.

Narrator 2: Soon the friends were back with the donkey.

Narrator 1: Jesus climbed on to the donkey and started to ride into the great city of Jerusalem.

Narrator 2: In no time the road was full of people.

Children enter and fill the front of the stage with their backs to the audience. They carry palm branches in their hands. The head of Jesus can be seen slowly moving past them—his body is hidden by the crowd, thus giving the effect of riding. He is accompanied by several disciples.

Narrator 1: They tore branches from the palm trees.

Narrator 2: They waved the branches and shouted as Jesus rode by.

The children wave palm branches.

★ SONG ONE ★

The palm song

(Tune: Here we go round the mulberry bush)

Here we go to Jerusalem,
Jerusalem, Jerusalem,
Here we go to Jerusalem,
Waving our palms for Jesus.

Here we go to Jerusalem,
Jerusalem, Jerusalem,
Here we go to Jerusalem,
With Jesus on a donkey.

Here we go to Jerusalem,
Jerusalem, Jerusalem,
Here we go to Jerusalem,
We're singing Alleluia.

Here we go to Jerusalem,
Jerusalem, Jerusalem,
Here we go to Jerusalem,
We're praising God in heaven.

Here we go to Jerusalem,
Jerusalem, Jerusalem,
Here we go to Jerusalem,
God bless the king of Israel.

The crowds leave the stage and only Jesus and the disciples are left.

Narrator 1: The day Jesus rode into Jerusalem we call Palm Sunday.

Narrator 2: Four days later, Jesus asked two more friends to do another job for him.

Jesus speaks to two of the disciples.

Narrator 1: 'Peter and John, please go and get our special meal ready for us,' Jesus said.

Narrator 2: 'But where are we going to eat it?' they asked.

Narrator 1: 'Go into the city,' said Jesus, 'and

you will meet a man carrying a jar of water.'

Narrator 2: 'Follow him to a house and get the meal ready there.'

All but Peter and John go off. A water carrier comes on with his jar, and the two follow him.

Narrator 1: Peter and John went to prepare for the Passover—a very special time for the people of Israel.

Peter and John prepare the meal. They will put wine and bread on the table. They are then joined by the others. All sit in an open semi-circle.

Narrator 2: Jesus and the other friends of Jesus joined Peter and John.

Narrator 1: During the meal Jesus got up, put a towel round his waist and poured water into a bowl.

Narrator 2: He then began washing the feet of his friends and dried them with the towel.

Jesus acts the foot-washing.

Washing song

(Tune: London Bridge is falling down)

Jesus Christ is kneeling down,
Kneeling down, kneeling down,
Jesus Christ is kneeling down,
King of heaven.

Jesus Christ is washing feet,
Washing feet, washing feet,
Jesus Christ is washing feet,
King of heaven.

Jesus Christ is drying feet,
Drying feet, drying feet,
Jesus Christ is drying feet,
King of heaven.

Not my feet but all of me,
All of me, all of me,
Not my feet but all of me,
Said Simon Peter.

Do the same for one another,
One another, one another.
Do the same for one another,
And God will bless you.

Narrator 1: After washing the feet of his friends, Jesus took some bread in his hands.

Narrator 2: 'Eat this and remember me,' he said.

Jesus lifts the bread.

Narrator 1: After the meal, Jesus took a cup of wine in his hands.

Jesus lifts the 'wine'.

Narrator 2: 'Drink this and remember me,' he said.

Narrator 1: And ever since, Christians have remembered Jesus in the bread and wine they are given in a special service called Holy Communion.

Narrator 2: Later that night, Jesus and his friends left the house where they had shared that special meal.

Jesus and friends walk slowly off the stage.

Narrator 1: Jesus took them to a garden outside the city.

Jesus and friends re-enter.

Narrator 2: Jesus knew that something very sad was going to happen.
Narrator 1: In the quiet of the garden, he prayed to God his Father.

Jesus moves away from his disciples and kneels, while his friends pretend to fall asleep. Silence is kept for a few moments. A noisy crowd then come running on.

Narrator 2: Suddenly the silence was broken by a crowd of people.
Narrator 1: Soldiers had come to take Jesus away.

Two soldiers lead Jesus away in one direction and the crowd follows. The friends of Jesus move off in the opposite direction. These two groups then form, one on either side of the stage, to sing the next song.

☆ SONG THREE ☆
....

Good Friday

(Tune: Michael row the boat ashore)

It is suggested that the groups sing alternate verses.

Friends
Jesus taken in the night,
Alleluia,
All his friends run off in fright,
Alleluia.

Crowd
Jesus stands before the priest,
Alleluia,
Dawn is breaking in the east,
Alleluia.

Friends
Pilate asks the question why,
Alleluia,
You want Jesus Christ to die,
Alleluia.

Crowd
People shout, 'It is because…'
Alleluia,
'he has broken all our laws.'
Alleluia.

For the next verse, the two groups form a line across the front of the stage. All the children will sing this verse. Behind the line, the top of a cross can be seen, carried by Jesus.

All
Jesus taken through the streets,
Alleluia.
Jeered and mocked by all he meets,
Alleluia.

Two groups re-form.

Crowd
Jesus hangs on cross of wood,
Alleluia,
On the day that we call Good,
Alleluia.

Friends
All is dark without the sun,
Alleluia,
Jesus dies; his work is done,
Alleluia.

Crowd
In the tomb that Joseph gave,
Alleluia,
Jesus rests there in the grave,
Alleluia.

Both groups remain on stage. Mary Magdalene enters and stands between the two groups.

Narrator 1: Jesus died on Good Friday, but something wonderful happened two days later.

Narrator 2: On Easter Day, a friend of Jesus called Mary went to the grave.

Narrator 1: Mary stood outside, crying.

Narrator 2: Jesus came up to her but she couldn't see him through her tears.

Jesus enters and walks over to Mary.

Narrator 1: Jesus said one word. He called her name. 'Mary.'

Narrator 2: Then Mary knew who it was. It was Jesus. He had kept his promise. He really was alive again.

Mary runs over to the group of disciples.

Narrator 1: And during the next few weeks, lots more of the friends of Jesus met him.

Jesus walks over to his friends in the group of disciples and greets them.

Jesus came there and named her, his voice now reclaimed her,
When she first set her eyes on Jesus again.
And she laughed through her tears; he answered her fears.
Singing, Jesus is risen, alive, alive-o.

Chorus…

Now back in the city, it was such a pity
That Thomas was missing when Jesus appeared.
'I'm afraid that I doubt him, can't believe without him.'
Singing, Jesus is risen, alive, alive-o.

Chorus…

Many years have gone by since they saw Jesus die,
And come back to life again, our risen Lord.
Thousands join in the chorus that Jesus restores us,
Singing, Jesus is risen, alive, alive-o.

☆ SONG FOUR ☆

Alive, alive-o

(Tune: Cockles and mussels)

All children are on stage to sing the final song.

In Jerusalem's city, where the garden's so pretty,
She first set her eyes on Jesus again.
Mary stood there a-crying, she'd seen Jesus dying.
Singing, Jesus is risen, alive, alive-o.

Chorus
Alive, alive-o, alive, alive-o,
Singing, Jesus is risen, alive, alive-o.

SAD DAD TO GLAD DAD!

This story is taken from Luke 15:11–32.

Jesus taught many things through the use of special stories called parables. The parables that Jesus told help us to learn more about God. This parable is about a son who runs away and a father who loves and forgives him.

Lots of people were crowding around, listening to Jesus. Some of them were saying that Jesus was friendly with people who did wrong things. Jesus told this story to teach them and us that God loves and forgives us. We have given the story a modern-day setting.

CAST AND PROPS

in order of appearance

Adult to introduce the play
Narrators 1 and 2
Dad
Older son (Jack)
Younger son (Sonny)
Cindy
Friends (no limit)
Children with pig masks (no limit)
Spade
Holiday brochure
Suitcase
Designer-style sweatshirts and trainers
Plates of food
A toy car or pedal car (optional)
A wallet
A job advertisement
A suit and shoes
A ring

Narrator 1: 'A father had two sons,' said Jesus.

Enter Dad.

Narrator 2: There was the older son. We'll call him Jack.

Older son enters from left side of stage, carrying a spade.

Narrator 1: And there was the younger son. We'll call him Sonny.

Younger son enters from right side of stage, carrying a holiday brochure.

Narrator 2: One day, Sonny asked his dad for his share of the family farm.

Narrator 1: His dad sold Sonny's share of the farm and gave him the money.

Narrator 2: Sonny packed his suitcase, said goodbye, and set off.

☆ SONG ONE ☆

The money song

(Tune: Sing a song of sixpence)

Now I'm packed and ready,
And waving Dad goodbye,
Off to have a good time,
What a lucky guy!
Soon be in the city,
Far away from Dad,
Shopping till I'm dropping—
That really can't be bad.

Narrator 1: His dad was very sad to see his son leave home.

☆ SONG TWO ☆

Dad's song

(Tune: Kum ba yah—sung twice)

Dad waves during song and then leaves stage.

Sonny's leaving, Lord, I'm so sad.
Sonny's leaving, Lord, I'm so sad.
Sonny's leaving, Lord, I'm so sad.
O Lord, I'm so sad.

Narrator 2: After a long journey, Sonny reached the bright city lights.

Enter Sonny, carrying a suitcase.

Narrator 1: Soon he was spending his money on…

Narrator 2: … new clothes…

Fashion show with models.

Narrator 1: … and new shoes…

Various trainers shown to Sonny.

Narrator 2: … posh nosh…

Plates of food are brought on.

Narrator 1: … a really fast car…

Bring on toy car or pedal car if available, or mime driving.

Narrator 1: … a girlfriend called Cindy…

Enter Cindy.

Narrator 1: … and a crowd of new friends.

Enter more children.

☆ SONG THREE ☆

Good times song

(Tune: Sing a song of sixpence)

Sing a song of good times,
A pocket full of cash.
Four and twenty new friends,
Going to a bash.
When it came to leaving,
My friends began to say,
Since I was in the money
I was the one to pay!

Narrator 2: But the day came when Sonny looked in his wallet and found…

Sonny looks at wallet.

Narrator 1: it was seriously empty!

★ SONG FOUR ★

There's a hole in my wallet

(Tune: There's a hole in my bucket)

The song is sung by two groups—Sonny is in one and Cindy in the other.

There's a hole in my wallet, dear Cindy, dear Cindy,
There's a hole in my wallet, dear Cindy, a hole.

Then fill it, dear Sonny, dear Sonny, dear Sonny,
Then fill it, dear Sonny, dear Sonny, fill it.

From where shall I fill it, dear Cindy, dear Cindy?
From where shall I fill it, dear Cindy, from where?

From the bank, dear Sonny, dear Sonny, dear Sonny,
From the bank, dear Sonny, dear Sonny, try the bank.

The bank has no money, dear Cindy, dear Cindy,
The bank has no money, dear Cindy, I'm broke!

Try Visa, dear Sonny, dear Sonny, dear Sonny,
Try Visa, dear Sonny, dear Sonny, use plastic!

But my card's been rejected, dear Cindy, dear Cindy,
My card's been rejected, dear Cindy, I'm broke.

Well, goodbye dear Sonny, dear Sonny, dear Sonny,
Well, goodbye dear Sonny, dear Sonny, I've gone.

There's a hole in my wallet, my wallet, my wallet,
There's a hole in my wallet, my money's all gone!

There's a hole in my wallet, my wallet, my wallet,
There's a hole in my wallet, my money's all gone!

Sonny leaves the stage on one side. Everyone else leaves on the other.

Narrator 1: Things went from bad to worse for Sonny.
Narrator 2: There was a food shortage in the land. That meant there was very little for anyone to eat…
Narrator 1: especially for those who had no money.
Narrator 2: Meanwhile, back at home, Sonny's dad never stopped thinking about him.

★ SONG TWO (REPRISE) ★

Dad's song

(Tune: Kum ba yah—sung twice)

Dad comes on and kneels down during song, then leaves stage.

I am praying, Lord, for my son,
I am praying, Lord, for my son,
I am praying, Lord, for my son,
O Lord, for my son.

Narrator 1: Far away from home, Sonny began to get very hungry.

Enter Sonny, rubbing his stomach.

Narrator 2: There was only one thing to do— get a job.
Narrator 1: But there was only one job going…

28

Narrator 2: 'Required—good pig man needed to feed a herd of pigs.'

Sonny holds up job advertisement.

Narrator 1: It was the only way to save his bacon.

Children with pig masks enter, singing 'The pig song'.

☆ SONG FIVE ☆

The pig song

(Tune: Three blind mice)

Adjust the number of pigs to the number of children.

Three hungry pigs,
Three hungry pigs,
See how they trot,
See how they trot,
They all trot after the farmer's son,
Who was sorry now for what he'd done.
'I wish my adventure had never begun,'
Thought one hungry son.

One hungry son,
One hungry son,
Why was he there?
Why was he there?
'I could be back home with Dad,
And say I'm sorry for being bad,
I'm sure it would help to make him glad,'
Thought one hungry son.

Narrator 1: Sonny knew that no one at home was ever hungry.
Narrator 2: So he waved goodbye to the pigs and set off.

Pigs leave one side. Sonny leaves the other side, but re-enters at once.

Narrator 1: This time his pockets were not full of money.

Sonny pulls pockets out of trousers.

Narrator 2: This time his clothes smelled like the pigs he had been looking after.

Sonny sniffs his clothes.

Narrator 1: This time he had to walk all the way.
Narrator 2: Back home, Sonny's dad never gave up hope that his son would come home.

☆ SONG TWO (REPRISE) ☆

Dad's song

(Tune: Kum ba yah—sung twice)

During the song, Dad comes on, looking for son, and remains on the side of the stage. Sonny stops walking while song is sung.

I am searching, Lord, for my son,
I am searching, Lord, for my son,
I am searching, Lord, for my son,
O Lord, for my son.

Narrator 1: As Sonny got nearer home, he began to wonder what his dad would do.

Narrator 2: Would his dad speak to him after what he had done?

Narrator 1: Would his dad be pleased to see him?

Narrator 2: Would his dad let him come home?

Narrator 1: While he was still a long way off, his dad saw him.

Dad gets excited when he sees Sonny.

Narrator 2: He began running towards the boy.

Narrator 1: He threw his arms round Sonny and kissed him.

Narrator 2: 'Dad,' said Sonny, 'I have let you down. I have done wrong things. I am very sorry.'

Narrator 1: But his son had come home and that made his dad very happy.

☆ SONG SIX ☆

The welcome home song

(Tune: Dance to your daddy—sung twice)

Dance with your daddy, my little laddie,
Dance with your daddy, my missing son.
You shall have a party, now get ready smartly,
You shall have a party, my missing son.
Dance with your daddy, my little laddie,
Dance with your daddy, my missing son.

Narrator 2: There was a huge party. Sonny was given…

Narrator 1: … the best suit in the house…

Enter servant with suit.

Narrator 2: … a new ring for his finger…

Enter servant with ring.

Narrator 1: … new shoes for his feet…

Enter servant with shoes.

Narrator 2: … and most of all… the love and forgiveness of his dad.

Father and son hug each other.

☆ SONG TWO (REPRISE) ☆

Dad's song

(Tune: Kum ba yah—sung twice)

All come on stage.

Great rejoicing now, my son's home,
Great rejoicing now, my son's home,
Great rejoicing now, my son's home,
O Lord, my son's home.

A PLACE IN THE SUN

This story is taken from Matthew 7:24–27.

Adult introduction

Jesus taught many things through the use of stories called parables. The stories that Jesus told help us to learn more about God. This story is about two men who each built a house.

During the adult introduction, Jesus enters and sits down at the front of the stage. As soon as he is seated, children come and sit around him. These children form the choir. On one side of the stage is a low block to represent the rock.

Narrator 1: There was once a man called Mr Wise.

Mr Wise enters left.

Narrator 2: And there was once a man called Mr Foolish.

Mr Foolish enters right.

Narrator 1: Now it so happened that they both wanted to build a new home.

Narrator 2: They both wanted a place in the sun where they could be happy and bring up their families.

Narrator 1: Mr Wise looked here…

Narrator 2: … and he looked there.

Narrator 1: Here was too low—the river might flood.

Narrator 2: There was too high—the wind might blow.

Narrator 1: After a long time, he found the right place.

Mr Wise stands by low block.

Narrator 2: It was not too low.

Narrator 1: It was not too high.

Narrator 2: There was solid rock to build on.

Narrator 1: It would make a strong foundation.

Narrators 1 & 2: It was just the right place.

Narrator 2: Mr Wise started to build his new house.

The house is constructed from pre-painted cardboard boxes which are brought on one at a time and laid on top of each other as the following song is sung. Any number of children can be builders.

☆ SONG ONE ☆

Mr Wise's song

(Tune: Old MacDonald had a farm)

Mr Wise he built a house,
Ee-i, ee-i, oh!
He started laying lots of bricks,
Ee-i, ee-i, oh!
With a big brick here,
And a small brick there,
Here a brick, there a brick,
Everywhere another brick.
Mr Wise he built a house,
Ee-i, ee-i, oh!

Mr Wise he built a house,
Ee-i, ee-i, oh!
And in this house he laid the floors,
Ee-i, ee-i, oh!
With a big bang here,
And a small bang there,
Here a bang, there a bang,
Everywhere another bang.
Mr Wise he built a house,
Ee-i, ee-i, oh!

Mr Wise he built a house,
Ee-i, ee-i, oh!
And on this house he put a roof,
Ee-i, ee-i, oh!
With a big tile here,
And a small tile there,
Here a tile, there a tile,
Everywhere another tile.
Mr Wise he built a house,
Ee-i, ee-i, oh!

Mr Wise he built a house,
Ee-i, ee-i, oh!
In the house went his family,
Ee-i, ee-i, oh!
With a big child here,
And a small child there,
Here a child, there a child,
Everywhere another child,
Mr Wise he built a house,
Ee-i, ee-i, oh!

During the last verse, builders leave the stage and Mr Wise fetches his family. They look at the house and then hide behind it.

Narrator 1: Mr Wise and his family settled very happily in the new home.

Narrator 2: Mr Foolish looked for a nice place to build his house.

Narrator 1: By the edge of the river was some sand. The children would like playing in the sand.

Two children unroll the river frieze on the opposite side of the stage to the rock.

Narrator 2: In the river there would be fish. He could go fishing in the river.

Narrator 1: There was no need to bother about digging down to the rock for a foundation.

Narrator 2: Nothing could go wrong here.

Narrator 1: It was just the right place. Or was it?

Narrator 2: Mr Foolish started to build his new house.

The house is constructed from pre-painted cardboard boxes which are brought on one at a time and laid on top of each other as the following song is sung. Any number of children can be builders.

☆ SONG TWO ☆

Mr Foolish's song

(Tune: This old man, he played one)

Foolish man, he laid one,
So the building was begun.

Chorus
With a quick-brick,
Far too slick,
Building much too fast.
Foolish house will never last.

Foolish man, he laid two,
Working hard, there's lots to do.

Chorus...

Foolish man, he laid three,
Stopping for a cup of tea.

Chorus...

Foolish man, he laid four,
Don't forget, you'll need a door!

Chorus...

Foolish man, he laid five,
Soon the family will arrive.

Chorus...

Foolish man, he laid six,
Soon be running out of bricks.

Chorus...

Foolish man, he laid seven,
Four more bricks will make eleven.

Chorus...

Foolish man, he laid eight,
He forgot to excavate.

Chorus...

Foolish man, he laid nine,
Half the bricks are out of line.

Chorus...

Foolish man, he laid ten,
Round the back to start again.

Chorus...

Builders leave the stage.

Narrator 3: Mr Foolish and Mr Wise walked around their new houses.

Narrator 4: Before long, they both felt a drop of rain.

Narrator 3: Soon it was more than a drop.

Narrator 4: Soon it was pouring with rain.

Narrator 3: Mr Wise watched as the rain poured down.

Narrator 4: He was glad he had built his house on a rock.

Narrator 3: Mr Foolish watched as the rain poured down.

Narrator 4: He was worried as the river got higher.

The rain song

(Tune: Pat-a-cake, pat-a-cake, baker's man)

Builders enter and stand by the house they built to sing the song, which should be sung three times, each time getting louder. Children may create a rain dance.

Pit-a-pat, pit-a-pat, drops of rain,
Back in my house as fast as I can,
Shut all the windows, and fasten the doors,
Keep snug and dry as down the rain pours.

Repeat twice more, getting louder each time.

Narrator 3: Mr Wise went round his house to see if the rain had come in. Everywhere was dry.

Pit-a-pat, pit-a-pat, drops of rain,
Back in my house as fast as I can,
Shut all the windows, and fasten the doors,
Keep snug and dry as down the rain pours.

Mr Wise holds up thumb as OK sign.

Narrator 4: Mr Foolish went round his house to see if the rain had come in. Everywhere was wet.

Mr Foolish makes appropriate actions to the following:

Narrator 3: The rain had come through the roof.
Narrator 4: The rain had come through the windows…
Narrator 3: … and the rain had come through the doors.
Narrator 4: Mr Foolish put on his wellies…
Narrator 3: … and his coat
Narrator 4: … and his hat.

Pit-a-pat, pit-a-pat, drops of rain,
Back in my house as fast as I can,
Shut all the windows, and fasten the doors,
I'm very wet as down the rain pours.

Narrator 3: Oh dear, things were not looking good for Mr Foolish and his house.
Narrator 4: As well as the wind and the rain, the river started to rise.

River frieze roll is lifted slowly from the floor.

Narrator 3: The water rose higher…
Narrator 4: … and higher…
Narrator 3: … and higher, until it…
Narrator 4: … flooded the house.
Narrator 3: Mr Wise looked out of his window.
Narrator 4: The trees were bending in the wind.
Narrator 3: Leaves were blowing about.
Narrator 4: Mr Foolish looked out of his window.

Mr Foolish looks up as high as possible.

Narrator 3: A tile blew off his roof.
Narrator 4: A door banged in the wind.
Narrator 3: His hat blew off his head.

Narrator 3: The rain came.
Narrator 4: The river rose.
Narrator 3: The wind blew and…
Narrator 4: … down fell Mr Foolish's house with a crash!

The house is pushed over by Mr Foolish and his family, who then stand around looking at it.

☆ SONG FIVE ☆

The poor foundation song

(Tune: Oh dear! What can the matter be?)

Oh, dear! What can the matter be?
Oh, dear! What can the matter be?
Oh, dear! What can the matter be?
It's all come crashing down.

You can't build a house without any foundations,
It's very important to choose good locations,
So you can build there for friends and relations,
And live happily ever more.

Oh, dear! What can the matter be?
Oh, dear! What can the matter be?
Oh, dear! What can the matter be?
It's all come crashing down.

It would be appropriate if, during this song, Mr Wise took Mr Foolish and his family into the Wises' house.

Narrator 3: Jesus said, 'Everyone who acts on these words of mine…
Narrator 4: … is like a wise man who builds his life on a rock.'
Narrator 3: When Jesus had finished saying these things, the crowds were amazed at his teaching…
Narrator 4: … because he spoke like someone who knew what he was talking about.

☆ SONG FOUR ☆

The wind song

(Tune: The wheels on the bus)

Sung twice, gradually getting louder. Children may perform a wind dance.

The wind on the house blows round and round,
Round and round, round and round,
The wind on the house blows round and round,
All through the night.

The tiles on the roof keep falling off,
Falling off, falling off,
The tiles on the roof keep falling off,
All through the night.

Windows in the house keep falling out,
Falling out, falling out,
Windows in the house keep falling out,
All through the night.

Bricks on the house keep falling down,
Falling down, falling down,
Bricks on the house keep falling down,
All through the night.

All involved in the presentation come on stage to sing the last song.

....

The good foundation song

(Tune: London Bridge is falling down)

The Foolish house has fallen down,
Fallen down, fallen down,
The Foolish house has fallen down,
No foundation.

The Wise house is standing strong,
Standing strong, standing strong,
The Wise house is standing strong,
Good foundation.

Listen now to Jesus' words,
Jesus' words, Jesus' words,
Listen now to Jesus' words,
Wise foundation.

Put in practice Jesus' words,
Jesus' words, Jesus' words,
Put in practice Jesus' words,
Best foundation.

During the last verse, Jesus leads everyone off stage.

GROWING UP

This story is taken from Mark 4:3–8.

CAST AND PROPS

in order of appearance

Adult to introduce the play
Jesus
Narrators 1 and 2
Farmers (the verses of the song 'One man went to sow' must be the same number as the number of farmers)
Dog (child with a mask)
Birds (children with masks and wings) (the verses of the song 'Five hungry birds' must be the same as the number of birds)
Plants (children wearing masks, or holding cut-out enlarged stalks of corn)
Sun bearer

Weeds (children wearing masks or holding cut-out enlarged weeds)
Good plants (all wearing masks or holding cut-out plant shapes)
Outline of the front of a boat
Low stool or chair
Roll of wallpaper or frieze paper painted with flowers and plants (Frieze A)
Smarties (to go on paper)
Roll of paper painted with rocks and cut to indicate rocks on one edge (Frieze B)
Sun (large cut-out on end of bamboo cane)

Adult introduction

One day, Jesus came and sat down by the side of Lake Galilee. Such large numbers of people gathered around him that he got into a boat and sat in it, while the people stayed by the shore.

Jesus taught many things through the use of stories called parables. The stories that Jesus told help us to learn more about God. This story is about a farmer.

The outline of the front of a boat is on stage. A low stool or chair is placed behind it. Jesus enters and sits down at the front of the stage. As soon as he is seated, children come and sit around him. When the children are seated, Jesus moves on to the boat (sitting on the stool or chair). The seated children form the choir.

Open the play with a harvest song of your choice.

Jesus remains sitting on the boat and is joined by the two narrators.

Narrator 1: It was springtime—the time to sow seeds so that later in the year there would be a harvest.
Narrator 2: The fields had been ploughed and the earth was ready for the seeds to be sown.
Narrator 1: Farmers were sowing their seeds in all the fields.

☆ SONG ONE ☆

One man went to sow

(Tune: One man went to mow)

The song begins with one farmer and his dog. More farmers enter with each new verse. They broadcast the seed as they walk up and down.

One man went to sow,
Went to sow a meadow.
One man and his dog—WOOF!
Went to sow a meadow.

Two men went to sow,
Went to sow their meadows,
Two men, one man and his dog—WOOF!
Went to sow their meadows.

Three men went to sow,
Went to sow their meadows,
Three men, two men, one man and his dog—
WOOF!
Went to sow their meadows.

Farmers leave. Birds enter and fly around.

Narrator 1: A flock of birds were flying around, watching the farmers sow their seeds.
Narrator 2: The birds were looking for food.

Frieze A is unwound horizontally. Smarties are placed on the paper.

Narrator 1: The birds saw that some seed had fallen on the path by the side of the field.

Birds rub their tummies and smile and fly around picking up and eating the Smarties.

☆ SONG TWO ☆

Five hungry birds

(Tune: Three blind mice)

Five hungry birds,
Five hungry birds,
See how they fly!
See how they fly!
They all flew after the farmer's seed,
And gobbled it up with amazing speed,
They'd never had such an enormous feed,
Those five hungry birds.

The song is sung twice. During the second verse, the birds fly off, very full and very slowly. As they leave, Frieze A is removed and Frieze B is unrolled vertically, showing the rocky outlines at the top. Children acting or holding plants in this scene crawl on behind Frieze B.

Narrator 1: Some of the seeds fell into very shallow, rocky soil.

☆ SONG THREE ☆

The rock song

(Tune: Hickory, dickory, dock)

Hickory, dickory, dock,
The plants will get a shock,
They'll grow quite high, but soon will die,
They can't live on a rock.

Narrator 2: There was no depth of earth in which they could grow.

Hickory, dickory, dock,
The plants will get a shock,
They'll grow quite high, but soon will die,
They can't live on a rock.

Narrator 1: They put down short roots and grew very quickly.

The plants grow quickly from behind Frieze B.

Hickory, dickory, dock,
The plants will get a shock,
They'll grow quite high, but soon will die,
They can't live on a rock.

Narrator 2: When the sun came up, the plants were scorched. Very soon they withered and died.

Enter child holding sun on bamboo cane. The sun rises slowly from the horizontal to the vertical. As it reaches the highest point, the plants slowly wither and lie down behind Frieze B.

☆ SONG FOUR ☆

Sun is shining

(Tune: London's burning—sung as a round)

Sun is shining, sun is shining,
Plants are drooping, plants are drooping;
No roots, no roots,
Plants are dying, plants are dying.

Children exit before Frieze B is removed. Frieze A is unwound vertically this time. Children, as plants, come on behind Frieze A. Weeds march on and barge their way in between the plants.

Narrator 1: Some of the seed fell where there were weeds and thorns.
Narrator 2: The plants grew up in the middle of the weeds and thorns.

The plant children need to be shorter than the weeds and thorns so that they are eventually hidden by the taller children.

☆ SONG FIVE ☆

The song of the weeds

(Tune: The grand old Duke of York)

Weeds march on the spot for the verse and move up and down to the chorus. The plants drop down with the weeds in the chorus but do not grow again. The song is sung twice.

We're the mighty thorns and weeds,
We grow so thick and tall
That other plants just have no chance,
We are the best of all.

Chorus

And when we are up, we are up,
And when we are down, we are down,
And when we are only half way up,
We are neither up nor down.

After the song, the weeds march off, and the plants leave from behind Frieze A.

Narrator 1: Some of the seed fell into good soil where it produced a crop—a hundred, 60 or 30 times what was sown.

All children come dancing on to the stage, dressed as plants or wearing masks.

☆ SONG SIX ☆

If you're happy and you're growing

(Tune: If you're happy and you know it)

Children do the actions.

If you're happy and you're growing, clap your hands,
If you're happy and you're growing, clap your hands,
If you're happy and you're growing
Where the farmer has been sowing,
If you're happy and you're growing, clap your hands.

If you're happy and you're growing, stamp your feet,
If you're happy and you're growing, stamp your feet,
If you're happy and you're growing
Where the farmer has been sowing,
If you're happy and you're growing, stamp your feet.

If you're happy and you're growing, shout 'Hurray!'
If you're happy and you're growing, shout 'Hurray!'
If you're happy and you're growing
Where the farmer has been sowing,
If you're happy and you're growing, shout 'Hurray!'

If you're happy and you're growing, do all three.
If you're happy and you're growing, do all three.
If you're happy and you're growing
Where the farmer has been sowing,
If you're happy and you're growing, do all three.

Narrator 2: And Jesus ended his story by saying…

Jesus stands up in the boat.

Jesus: If you have ears to hear, pay attention.

☆ SONG SEVEN ☆

Ears to hear

(Tune: Kum ba yah)

This song is sung as a prayer.

Ears to hear, Lord, ears to hear!
Ears to hear, Lord, ears to hear!
Ears to hear, Lord, ears to hear!
O Lord, ears to hear.

Hands to work, Lord, hands to work!
Hands to work, Lord, hands to work!
Hands to work, Lord, hands to work!
O Lord, hands to work.

Feet to go, Lord, feet to go!
Feet to go, Lord, feet to go!
Feet to go, Lord, feet to go!
O Lord, feet to go!

Hearts to love, Lord, hearts to love!
Hearts to love, Lord, hearts to love!
Hearts to love, Lord, hearts to love!
O Lord, hearts to love!

APPENDIX ONE

COMPLETE SET OF THE SONGS

A CELEBRATION OF CREATION

★1

It was good

(Tune: The farmer's in his den)

The light is shining bright,
The light is shining bright,
God saw that it was good,
The light is shining bright.

The sky is in the heavens,
The sky is in the heavens,
God saw that it was good,
The sky is in the heavens.

God made the land and sea,
God made the land and sea,
God saw that they were good,
God made the land and sea.

God made the sun and moon,
God made the sun and moon,
God saw that they were good,
God made the sun and moon.

God made the fish and birds,
God made the fish and birds,
God saw that they were good,
God made the fish and birds.

God made the animals,
God made the animals,
God saw that they were good,
God made the animals.

God made the people too,
God made the people too,
God saw that we were good,
God made the people too.

Night and day

(Tune: Jack and Jill)

All was black, and all was dark,
When God began creation,
Nothing could be seen at all,
There was no variation.

Let light shine, commanded God,
And soon the light was shining.
Light is day, the dark is night,
(line sung in two halves by the two groups)
It's part of my designing.

Thanks to God we have them still,
It's part of his plan for us;
So alleluia, praise the Lord,
Let all join in this chorus.

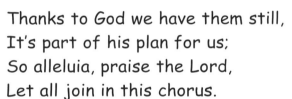

⭐ 3

Sky-sea song

(Tune: London Bridge is falling down)

Lots of water everywhere,
Everywhere, everywhere,
Lots of water everywhere,
Make a dome now.

Place the sky high in the heavens,
In the heavens, in the heavens,
Place the sky high in the heavens,
Above the water.

Let clouds float across the sky,
Across the sky, across the sky,
Let clouds float across the sky,
High in the heavens.

The plant song

(Tune: Old MacDonald had a farm)

Father God he made the land,
Praise, oh praise his name!
And on this land he grew some plants,
Praise, oh praise his name!
With a rose bush here,
A busy lizzie there,
Here a plant, there a plant,
Everywhere another plant.
Father God he made the land,
Praise, oh praise his name!

Father God he made the land,
Praise, oh praise his name!
And on this land he grew some trees,
Praise, oh praise his name!
With an apple tree here,
A cherry tree there,
Here some fruit, there some fruit,
Everywhere some other fruit.
Father God he made the land,
Praise, oh praise his name!

Father God he made the land,
Praise, oh praise his name!
And on this land he grew some grain,
Praise, oh praise his name!
With a wheat field here,
And a maize field there,
Here some corn, there some corn,
Everywhere golden corn.
Father God he made the land,
Praise, oh praise his name!

5

The sun and the moon song

(Tune: Michael Finnegan)

And God commanded, 'Do what I say again,
A light, very bright, to shine in the day again.'
He looked at the light and said, 'OK' again,
In God's perfect way again, shine again.

I need a light that's not so bright again,
A light, not so bright, to shine in the night again,
He looked at the light and said, 'That's right' again,
Up there in the height again, shine again.

Up in the sky God fixed tiny stars again,
Saturn, Jupiter, Venus and Mars again,
Then he shouted 'hip hip hoorahs' again.
With extra loud 'oompahs' again, shine again.

The sea creatures and birds

(Tune: Green grow the rushes-o)

We'll sing you one-o,
Deep are the oceans-o.
What is your one-o?
One's a shark with big white teeth and ever more shall be so.

We'll sing you two-o,
High are the heavens-o.
What are your two-o?
Two's a blackbird in a tree, singing all the day-o.
One's a shark with big white teeth and ever more shall be so.

We'll sing you three-o,
Deep are the oceans-o.
What are your three-o?
Three, three, the turtle.
Two's a blackbird in a tree, singing all the day-o.
One's a shark with big white teeth and ever more shall be so.

We'll sing you four-o,
High are the heavens-o.
What are your four-o?
Four for the eagle flying high.
Three, three, the turtle.
Two's a blackbird in a tree, singing all the day-o.
One's a shark with big white teeth and ever more shall be so.

Reproduced with permission from *Sing a Song of Seasons* published by BRF 2005 (1 84101 364 1)

We'll sing you five-o,
Deep are the oceans-o.
What are your five-o?
Five for the dolphin playing tricks,
And four for the eagle flying high.
Three, three, the turtle.
Two's a blackbird in a tree, singing all the day-o.
One's a shark with big white teeth and ever more shall be so.

We'll sing you six-o,
High are the heavens-o.
What are your six-o?
Six for the six swooping swallows,
Five for the dolphin playing tricks,
And four for the eagle flying high.
Three, three, the turtle.
Two's a blackbird in a tree, singing all the day-o.
One's a shark with big white teeth and ever more shall be so.

We'll sing you seven-o,
Deep are the oceans-o,
What are your seven-o?
Seven for the seven whales swimming deep,
And six for the six swooping swallows,
Five for the dolphin playing tricks,
And four for the eagle flying high.
Three, three, the turtle.
Two's a blackbird in a tree, singing all the day-o.
One's a shark with big white teeth and ever more shall be so.

We'll sing you eight-o,
High are the heavens-o,
What are your eight-o?
Eight for the robin redbreast,
Seven for the seven whales swimming deep,
And six for the six swooping swallows,
Five for the dolphin playing tricks,
And four for the eagle flying high.
Three, three, the turtle.
Two's a blackbird in a tree, singing all the day-o.
One's a shark with big white teeth and ever more shall be so.

We'll sing you nine-o,
Deep are the oceans-o.
What are your nine-o?
Nine for the nine crawling crabs,
Eight for the robin redbreast,
Seven for the seven whales swimming deep,
And six for the six swooping swallows,
Five for the dolphin playing tricks,
And four for the eagle flying high.
Three, three, the turtle.
Two's a blackbird in a tree, singing all the day-o.
One's a shark with big white teeth and ever more shall be so.

We'll sing you ten-o,
High are the heavens-o.
What are your ten-o?
Ten for the ten loud cuckoos,
Nine for the nine crawling crabs,
Eight for the robin redbreast,
Seven for the seven whales swimming deep,
And six for the six swooping swallows,
Five for the dolphin playing tricks,
And four for the eagle flying high.
Three, three, the turtle.
Two's a blackbird in a tree, singing all the day-o.
One's a shark with big white teeth and ever more shall be so.

Reproduced with permission from *Sing a Song of Seasons* published by BRF 2005 (1 84101 364 1)

Animals everywhere

(Tune: He's got the whole world in his hands)

He made the creepy crawly spider with his hands,
He made the creepy crawly spider with his hands,
He made the creepy crawly spider with his hands,
He made the whole world with his hands.

He made the snugly cuddly rabbit with his hands,
He made the snugly cuddly rabbit with his hands,
He made the snugly cuddly rabbit with his hands,
He made the whole world with his hands.

He made the humpy dumpy camel with his hands,
He made the humpy dumpy camel with his hands,
He made the humpy dumpy camel with his hands,
He made the whole world with his hands.

He made the happy snappy crocodile with his hands,
He made the happy snappy crocodile with his hands,
He made the happy snappy crocodile with his hands,
He made the whole world with his hands.

He made the jumpy bumpy puppy with his hands,
He made the jumpy bumpy puppy with his hands,
He made the jumpy bumpy puppy with his hands,
He made the whole world with his hands.

He made the perky quirky turkey with his hands,
He made the perky quirky turkey with his hands,
He made the perky quirky turkey with his hands,
He made the whole world with his hands.

He made the podgy splodgy piggy with his hands,
He made the podgy splodgy piggy with his hands,
He made the podgy splodgy piggy with his hands,
He made the whole world with his hands.

He made the swinging clinging monkey with his hands,
He made the swinging clinging monkey with his hands,
He made the swinging clinging monkey with his hands,
He made the whole world with his hands.

The seven days of creation

(Tune: The Twelve Days of Christmas)

On the first day of creation
the good Lord gave away
Light and darkness, night and day.

On the second day of creation
the good Lord gave away
Sky and water,
Light and darkness, night and day.

On the third day of creation
the good Lord gave away
Land, sea and plants,
Sky and water,
Light and darkness, night and day.

On the fourth day of creation
the good Lord gave away
Sun, moon and stars,
Land, sea and plants,
Sky and water,
Light and darkness, night and day.

On the fifth day of creation
the good Lord gave away
Birds and sea creatures,
Sun, moon and stars,
Land, sea and plants,
Sky and water,
Light and darkness, night and day.

On the sixth day of creation
the good Lord gave away
Animals and humans,
Birds and sea creatures,
Sun, moon and stars,
Land, sea and plants,
Sky and water,
Light and darkness, night and day.

On the seventh day of creation
the good Lord gave away,
One day of rest,
Animals and humans,
Birds and sea creatures,
Sun, moon and stars,
Land, sea and plants,
Sky and water,
Light and darkness, night and day.

PALM TREES TO EASTER GARDEN

The palm song

(Tune: Here we go round the mulberry bush)

Here we go to Jerusalem,
Jerusalem, Jerusalem,
Here we go to Jerusalem,
Waving our palms for Jesus.

Here we go to Jerusalem,
Jerusalem, Jerusalem,
Here we go to Jerusalem,
With Jesus on a donkey.

Here we go to Jerusalem,
Jerusalem, Jerusalem,
Here we go to Jerusalem,
We're singing Alleluia.

Here we go to Jerusalem,
Jerusalem, Jerusalem,
Here we go to Jerusalem,
We're praising God in heaven.

Here we go to Jerusalem,
Jerusalem, Jerusalem,
Here we go to Jerusalem,
God bless the king of Israel.

 Reproduced with permission from *Sing a Song of Seasons* published by BRF 2005 (1 84101 364 1)

Washing song

(Tune: London Bridge is falling down)

Jesus Christ is kneeling down,
Kneeling down, kneeling down,
Jesus Christ is kneeling down,
King of heaven.

Jesus Christ is washing feet,
Washing feet, washing feet,
Jesus Christ is washing feet,
King of heaven.

Jesus Christ is drying feet,
Drying feet, drying feet,
Jesus Christ is drying feet,
King of heaven.

Not my feet but all of me,
All of me, all of me,
Not my feet but all of me,
Said Simon Peter.

Do the same for one another,
One another, one another.
Do the same for one another,
And God will bless you.

Good Friday

(Tune: Michael row the boat ashore)

Jesus taken in the night,
Alleluia,
All his friends run off in fright,
Alleluia.

Jesus stands before the priest,
Alleluia,
Dawn is breaking in the east,
Alleluia.

Pilate asks the question why,
Alleluia,
You want Jesus Christ to die,
Alleluia.

People shout, 'It is because...'
Alleluia,
'he has broken all our laws.'
Alleluia.

Jesus taken through the streets,
Alleluia.
Jeered and mocked by all he meets,
Alleluia.

Jesus hangs on cross of wood,
Alleluia,
On the day that we call Good,
Alleluia.

All is dark without the sun,
Alleluia,
Jesus dies; his work is done,
Alleluia.

In the tomb that Joseph gave,
Alleluia,
Jesus rests there in the grave,
Alleluia.

Alive, alive-o

(Tune: Cockles and mussels)

In Jerusalem's city, where the garden's so pretty,
She first set her eyes on Jesus again.
Mary stood there a-crying, she'd seen Jesus dying.
Singing, Jesus is risen, alive, alive-o.

Chorus
Alive, alive-o, alive, alive-o,
Singing, Jesus is risen, alive, alive-o.

Jesus came there and named her, his voice now reclaimed her,
When she first set her eyes on Jesus again.
And she laughed through her tears; he answered her fears.
Singing, Jesus is risen, alive, alive-o.

Chorus...

Now back in the city, it was such a pity
That Thomas was missing when Jesus appeared.
'I'm afraid that I doubt him, can't believe without him.'
Singing, Jesus is risen, alive, alive-o.

Chorus...

Many years have gone by since they saw Jesus die,
And come back to life again, our risen Lord.
Thousands join in the chorus that Jesus restores us,
Singing, Jesus is risen, alive, alive-o.

SAD DAD TO GLAD DAD!

★ 1

The money song

(Tune: Sing a song of sixpence)

Now I'm packed and ready,
And waving Dad goodbye,
Off to have a good time,
What a lucky guy!
Soon be in the city,
Far away from Dad,
Shopping till I'm dropping—
That really can't be bad.

Reproduced with permission from *Sing a Song of Seasons* published by BRF 2005 (1 84101 364 1)

★2 Dad's song

(Tune: Kum ba yah—each verse sung twice)

Sonny's leaving, Lord, I'm so sad.
Sonny's leaving, Lord, I'm so sad.
Sonny's leaving, Lord, I'm so sad.
O Lord, I'm so sad.

I am praying, Lord, for my son,
I am praying, Lord, for my son,
I am praying, Lord, for my son,
O Lord, for my son.

I am searching, Lord, for my son,
I am searching, Lord, for my son,
I am searching, Lord, for my son,
O Lord, for my son.

Great rejoicing now, my son's home,
Great rejoicing now, my son's home,
Great rejoicing now, my son's home,
O Lord, my son's home.

★3 Good times song

(Tune: Sing a song of sixpence)

Sing a song of good times,
A pocket full of cash.
Four and twenty new friends,
Going to a bash.
When it came to leaving,
My friends began to say,
Since I was in the money
I was the one to pay!

There's a hole in my wallet

(Tune: There's a hole in my bucket)

There's a hole in my wallet, dear Cindy, dear Cindy,
There's a hole in my wallet, dear Cindy, a hole.

Then fill it, dear Sonny, dear Sonny, dear Sonny,
Then fill it dear Sonny, dear Sonny, fill it.

From where shall I fill it, dear Cindy, dear Cindy?
From where shall I fill it, dear Cindy, from where?

From the bank, dear Sonny, dear Sonny, dear Sonny,
From the bank, dear Sonny, dear Sonny, try the bank.

The bank has no money, dear Cindy, dear Cindy,
The bank has no money, dear Cindy, I'm broke!

Try Visa, dear Sonny, dear Sonny, dear Sonny,
Try Visa, dear Sonny, dear Sonny, use plastic!

But my card's been rejected, dear Cindy, dear Cindy,
My card's been rejected, dear Cindy, I'm broke.

Well, goodbye dear Sonny, dear Sonny, dear Sonny,
Well, goodbye dear Sonny, dear Sonny, I've gone.

There's a hole in my wallet, my wallet, my wallet,
There's a hole in my wallet, my money's all gone!

There's a hole in my wallet, my wallet, my wallet,
There's a hole in my wallet, my money's all gone!

Reproduced with permission from *Sing a Song of Seasons* published by BRF 2005 (1 84101 364 1)

The pig song

(Tune: Three blind mice)

Three hungry pigs,
Three hungry pigs,
See how they trot,
See how they trot,
They all trot after the farmer's son,
Who was sorry now for what he'd done.
'I wish my adventure had never begun,'
Thought one hungry son.

One hungry son,
One hungry son,
Why was he there?
Why was he there?
'I could be back home with Dad,
And say I'm sorry for being bad,
I'm sure it would help to make him glad,'
Thought one hungry son.

The welcome home song

(Tune: Dance to your daddy—sung twice)

Dance with your daddy, my little laddie,
Dance with your daddy, my missing son.
You shall have a party, now get ready smartly,
You shall have a party, my missing son.
Dance with your daddy, my little laddie,
Dance with your daddy, my missing son.

A PLACE IN THE SUN

★1 Mr Wise's song

(Tune: Old MacDonald had a farm)

Mr Wise he built a house,
Ee-i, ee-i, oh!
He started laying lots of bricks,
Ee-i, ee-i, oh!
With a big brick here,
And a small brick there,
Here a brick, there a brick,
Everywhere another brick.
Mr Wise he built a house,
Ee-i, ee-i, oh!

Mr Wise he built a house,
Ee-i, ee-i, oh!
And in this house he laid the floors,
Ee-i, ee-i, oh!
With a big bang here,
And a small bang there,
Here a bang, there a bang,
Everywhere another bang.
Mr Wise he built a house,
Ee-i, ee-i, oh!

Mr Wise he built a house,
Ee-i, ee-i, oh!
And on this house he put a roof,
Ee-i, ee-i, oh!
With a big tile here,
And a small tile there,
Here a tile, there a tile,
Everywhere another tile.
Mr Wise he built a house,
Ee-i, ee-i, oh!

Mr Wise he built a house,
Ee-i, ee-i, oh!
In the house went his family,
Ee-i, ee-i, oh!
With a big child here,
And a small child there,
Here a child, there a child,
Everywhere another child,
Mr Wise he built a house,
Ee-i, ee-i, oh!

Mr Foolish's song

(Tune: This old man, he played one)

Foolish man, he laid one,
So the building was begun.

> Chorus
> With a quick-brick,
> Far too slick,
> Building much too fast.
> Foolish house will never last.

Foolish man, he laid two,
Working hard, there's lots to do.

Chorus...

Foolish man, he laid three,
Stopping for a cup of tea.

Chorus...

Foolish man, he laid four,
Don't forget, you'll need a door!

Chorus...

Foolish man, he laid five,
Soon the family will arrive.

Chorus...

Foolish man, he laid six,
Soon be running out of bricks.

Chorus...

Foolish man, he laid seven,
Four more bricks will make eleven.

Chorus...

Foolish man, he laid eight,
He forgot to excavate.

Chorus...

Foolish man, he laid nine,
Half the bricks are out of line.

Chorus...

Foolish man, he laid ten,
Round the back to start again.

Chorus...

The rain song

(Tune: Pat-a-cake, pat-a-cake, baker's man)

Pit-a-pat, pit-a-pat, drops of rain,
Back in my house as fast as I can,
Shut all the windows, and fasten the doors,
Keep snug and dry as down the rain pours.

Pit-a-pat, pit-a-pat, drops of rain,
Back in my house as fast as I can,
Shut all the windows, and fasten the doors,
I'm very wet as down the rain pours.

The wind song

(Tune: The wheels on the bus)

The wind on the house blows round
and round,
Round and round, round and round,
The wind on the house blows round
and round,
All through the night.

The tiles on the roof keep falling off,
Falling off, falling off,
The tiles on the roof keep falling off,
All through the night.

Windows in the house keep falling out,
Falling out, falling out,
Windows in the house keep falling out,
All through the night.

Bricks on the house keep falling down,
Falling down, falling down,
Bricks on the house keep falling down,
All through the night.

The poor foundation song

(Tune: Oh, dear! What can the matter be?)

Oh, dear! What can the matter be?
Oh, dear! What can the matter be?
Oh, dear! What can the matter be?
It's all come crashing down.

You can't build a house without any foundations,
It's very important to choose good locations,
So you can build there for friends and relations,
And live happily ever more.

Oh, dear! What can the matter be?
Oh, dear! What can the matter be?
Oh, dear! What can the matter be?
It's all come crashing down.

The good foundation song

(Tune: London Bridge is falling down)

The Foolish house has fallen down,
Fallen down, fallen down,
The Foolish house has fallen down,
No foundation.

The Wise house is standing strong,
Standing strong, standing strong,
The Wise house is standing strong,
Good foundation.

Listen now to Jesus' words,
Jesus' words, Jesus' words,
Listen now to Jesus' words,
Wise foundation.

Put in practice Jesus' words,
Jesus' words, Jesus' words,
Put in practice Jesus' words,
Best foundation.

GROWING UP

★ 1

One man went to sow

(Tune: One man went to mow)

One man went to sow,
Went to sow a meadow,
One man and his dog—WOOF!
Went to sow a meadow.

Two men went to sow,
Went to sow their meadows,
Two men, one man and his dog—
WOOF!
Went to sow their meadows.

Three men went to sow,
Went to sow their meadows,
Three men, two men, one man and his
dog—WOOF!
Went to sow their meadows.

★ 2

Five hungry birds

(Tune: Three blind mice)

Five hungry birds,
Five hungry birds,
See how they fly!
See how they fly!
They all flew after the farmer's seed,
And gobbled it up with amazing speed,
They'd never had such an enormous feed,
Those five hungry birds.

 Reproduced with permission from *Sing a Song of Seasons* published by BRF 2005 (1 84101 364 1)

★3

The rock song

(Tune: Hickory, dickory, dock)

Hickory, dickory, dock,
The plants will get a shock,
They'll grow quite high, but soon will die,
They can't live on a rock.

★4

Sun is shining

(Tune: London's burning—sung as a round)

Sun is shining, sun is shining,
Plants are drooping, plants are drooping;
No roots, no roots,
Plants are dying, plants are dying.

★5

The song of the weeds

(Tune: The Grand old Duke of York)

We're the mighty thorns and weeds,
We grow so thick and tall
That other plants just have no chance,
We are the best of all.

Chorus
And when we are up, we are up,
And when we are down, we are down,
And when we are only half way up,
We are neither up nor down.

If you're happy and you're growing

(Tune: If you're happy and you know it)

If you're happy and you're growing, clap your hands,
If you're happy and you're growing, clap your hands,
If you're happy and you're growing
Where the farmer has been sowing,
If you're happy and you're growing, clap your hands.

If you're happy and you're growing, stamp your feet,
If you're happy and you're growing, stamp your feet,
If you're happy and you're growing
Where the farmer has been sowing,
If you're happy and you're growing, stamp your feet.

If you're happy and you're growing, shout 'Hurray!'
If you're happy and you're growing, shout 'Hurray!'
If you're happy and you're growing
Where the farmer has been sowing,
If you're happy and you're growing, shout 'Hurray!'

If you're happy and you're growing, do all three,
If you're happy and you're growing, do all three,
If you're happy and you're growing
Where the farmer has been sowing,
If you're happy and you're growing, do all three.

 Reproduced with permission from *Sing a Song of Seasons* published by BRF 2005 (1 84101 364 1)

Ears to hear

(Tune: Kum ba yah)

Ears to hear, Lord, ears to hear!
Ears to hear, Lord, ears to hear!
Ears to hear, Lord, ears to hear!
O Lord, ears to hear.

Hands to work, Lord, hands to work!
Hands to work, Lord, hands to work!
Hands to work, Lord, hands to work!
O Lord, hands to work.

Feet to go, Lord, feet to go!
Feet to go, Lord, feet to go!
Feet to go, Lord, feet to go!
O Lord, feet to go!

Hearts to love, Lord, hearts to love!
Hearts to love, Lord, hearts to love!
Hearts to love, Lord, hearts to love!
O Lord, hearts to love!

APPENDIX TWO

MUSIC SCORES FOR THE NURSERY RHYME TUNES

A CELEBRATION OF CREATION

Song One: It was good

(Tune: The farmer's in his den)

Song Two: Night and day

(Tune: Jack and Jill)

Song Three: Sky-sea song

(Tune: London Bridge is falling down)

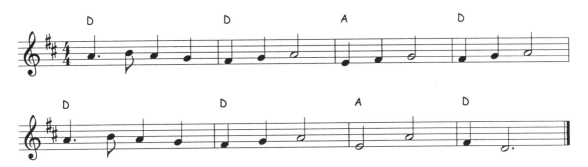

Song Four: The plant song

(Tune: Old MacDonald had a farm)

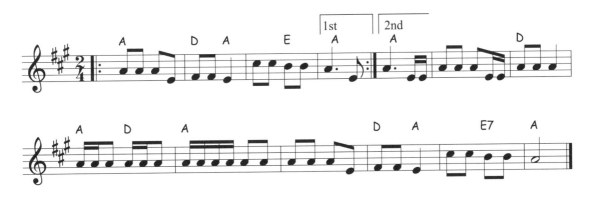

Song Five: The sun and the moon song

(Tune: Michael Finnegan)

75

Song Six: The sea creatures and birds

(Tune: Green grow the rushes-o)

Song Seven: Animals everywhere

(Tune: He's got the whole world in his hands)

Song Eight: The seven days of creation

(Tune: The Twelve Days of Christmas)

PALM TREES TO EASTER GARDEN

Song One: The palm song

(Tune: Here we go round the mulberry bush)

Song Two: Washing song

(Tune: London Bridge is falling down)

Song Three: Good Friday

(Tune: Michael row the boat ashore)

Song Four: Alive, alive-o

(Tune: Cockles and mussels)

SAD DAD TO GLAD DAD!

Song One: The money song

(Tune: Sing a song of sixpence)

Song Two: Dad's song

(Tune: Kum ba yah)

Song Three: Good times song

(Tune: Sing a song of sixpence)

Song Four: There's a hole in my wallet

(Tune: There's a hole in my bucket)

Song Five: The pig song

(Tune: Three blind mice)

Song Six: The welcome home song

(Tune: Dance to your daddy)

A PLACE IN THE SUN

Song One: Mr Wise's song

(Tune: Old MacDonald had a farm)

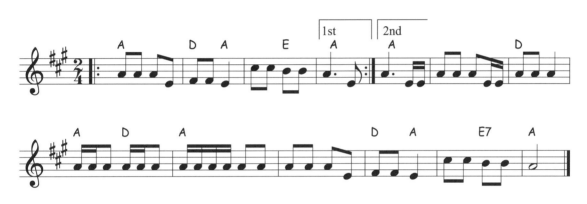

Song Two: Mr Foolish's song

(Tune: This old man, he played one)

Song Three: The rain song

(Tune: Pat-a-cake, pat-a-cake, baker's man)

Song Four: The wind song

(Tune: The wheels on the bus)

Song Five: The poor foundation song

(Tune: Oh, dear! What can the matter be?)

Song Six: The good foundation song

(Tune: London Bridge is falling down)

GROWING UP

Song One: One man went to sow

(Tune: One man went to mow)

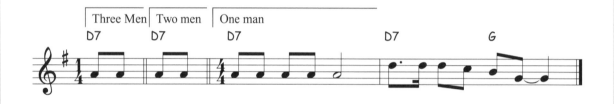

Song Two: Five hungry birds

(Tune: Three blind mice)

Song Three: The rock song

(Tune: Hickory, dickory, dock)

Song Four: Sun is shining

(Tune: London's burning)

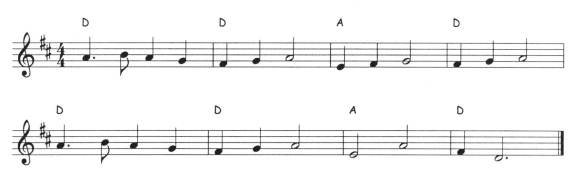

Song Five: The song of the weeds

(Tune: The Grand old Duke of York)

Song Six: If you're happy and you're growing

(Tune: If you're happy and you know it)

Song Seven: Ears to hear

(Tune: Kum ba yah)

APPENDIX THREE

CRAFT TEMPLATES

Cloud shape

Bird shape

Star shape

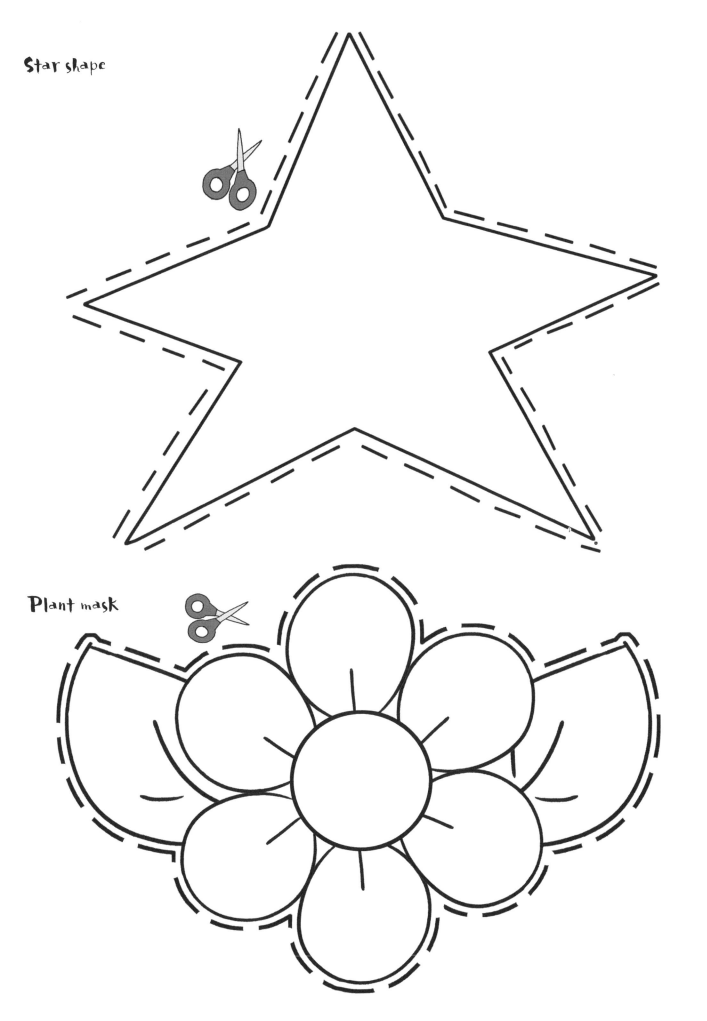

Plant mask

Animal mask

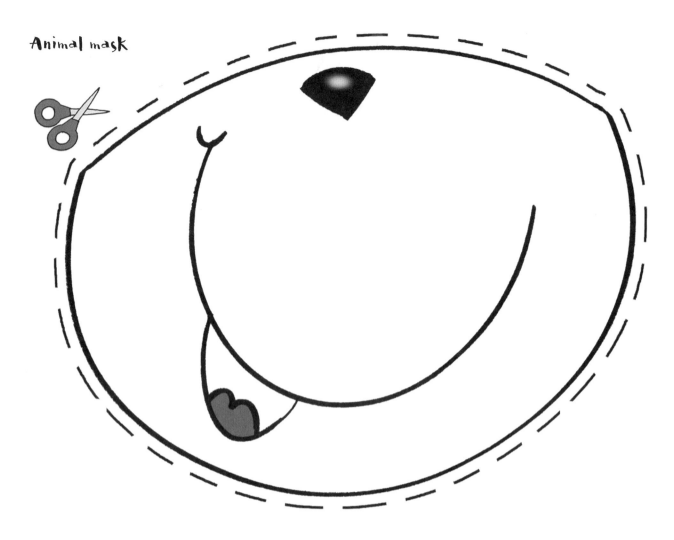

A PLACE IN THE SUN

Fun fish for river frieze

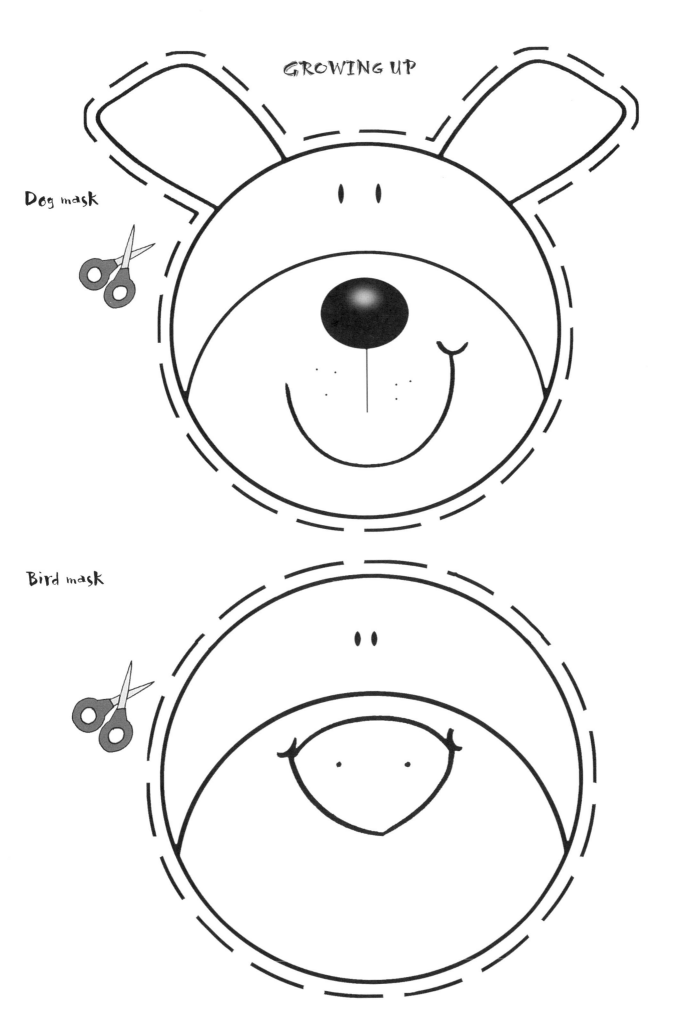

Dog mask

Bird mask

Plant mask

Sun mask

Weed mask

Sun shape

 Reproduced with permission from *Sing a Song of Seasons* published by BRF 2005 (1 84101 364 1)

Outline of the front of a boat

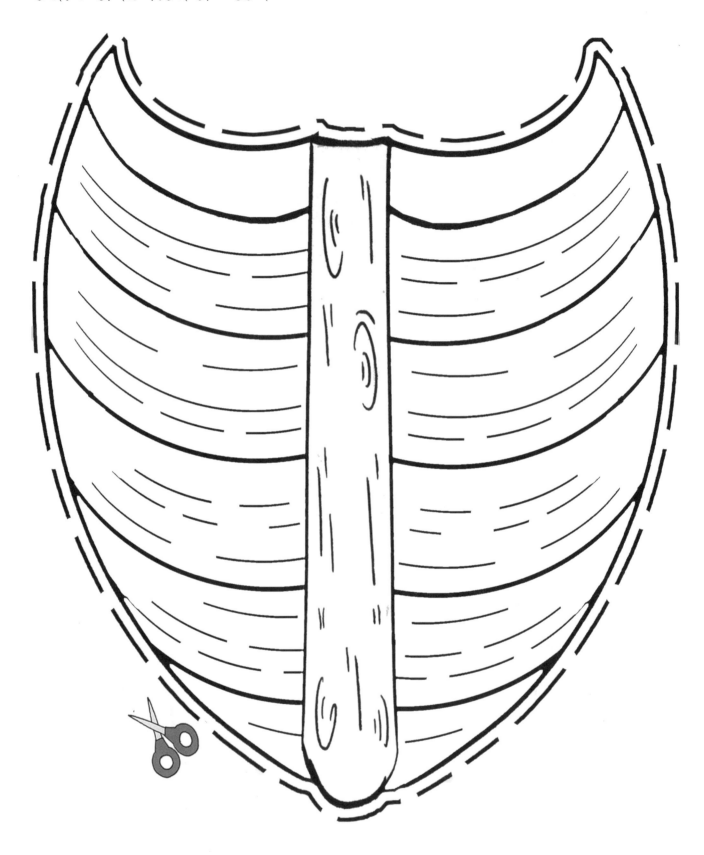

Trace or copy on to card, enlarging to desired size. Cut out and paint as desired.